SO YOU'RE GOING ON A TRIP?

WHAT FUN!

KID'S TRAVEL FUN BOOK

LORIS & MARLIN BREE

SCHOLASTIC INC.

New York Toronto London Auckland Sydney
Mexico City New Delhi Hong Kong

KID'S
TRAVEL FUN
BOOK

ISBN 0-439-22432-2

Copyright © 2000 by Loris Bree and Marlin Bree.
Illustrations by Marlin Bree.
All rights reserved.
Published by Scholastic Inc., 555 Broadway, New York, NY 10012,
by arrangement with Marlor Press Inc.
SCHOLASTIC and associated logos are trademarks and/or
registered trademarks of Scholastic Inc.

12 11 10 9 8 7 6 5 4 3 2 1   1 2 3 4 5 6/0

Printed in the U.S.A.   23

First Scholastic printing, June 2001

C O N T E N T S

GOING ON A TRIP?

WHERE ARE YOU GOING ?

Pacific bience center

WHERE IS IT LOCATED?

seattle

DRAW SOME   WINGS ON US

Flap! Flap! Hey, are we making the right sound?

LUCKY ME! I'LL BE GOING BY
(CIRCLE THE RIGHT ONE)

PLANE

TRAIN

CAR

BALLOON

SHIP   or DOGSLED

I'LL BE GONE
THIS LONG
1 day
DAYS

THESE PEOPLE WILL BE
COMING WITH ME (LUCKY THEM)

the whole Mac program in
Franklin Elementry.

ARE WE THERE YET?

DRAW A MAP OF WHERE YOU'RE GOING. YOU CAN DO IT!

Talk to your adults. See their map. You can draw your own

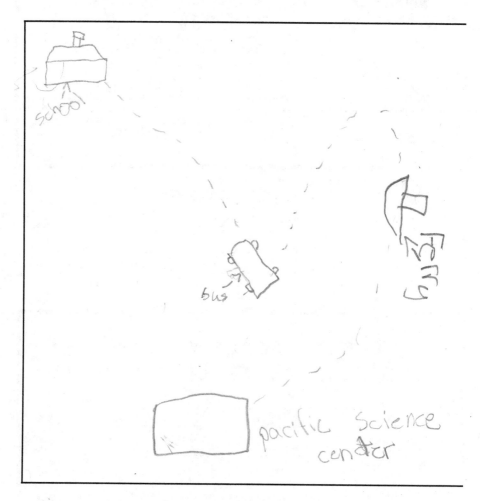

Helpful hints: Draw where you will start from Show where you'll be going. If you're going to make stops along the way, draw that in, too.

Here's an example of what a kid's map looks like. Draw your own. Your adults can help.

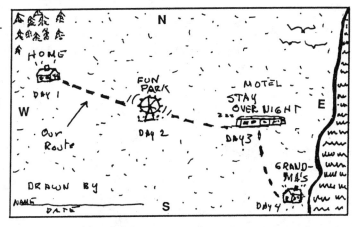

Label your stops. Connect the stops with a line. Hey, now you've got your own map. Remember to ask, in a loud voice: ARE WE THERE YET? (Parents like to be asked this question) Wave *your* map at them.

FUN
THINGS
TO DO
WHEN
I GET
THERE

Here's my list of things I want to do on this trip.

(You can do a little research on your trip on the internet, in books, or in the library, with the help of your adults)

1 Movie

2 Buterfly gardens.

3

4

5

6

7

WHICH BUG IS DIFFERENT?

DANDY ROAD SIGNS

Here are some fun signs. One of the signs below
is a real sign. Can you pick the real one?*

DISAGREE
ZONE

NO RAIN
PERMITTED TODAY

DO NOT FEED
THE DINOSAUR

STOP RIGHT NOW!

BEAM ME UP,
SCOTTY

CHECK YOUR MAP. YOU
MAY BE OFF THE ROUTE

The "stop" sign is the real one. Look for its white letters on a red face.

WHAT I WANT TO TAKE ALONG TO HAVE FUN

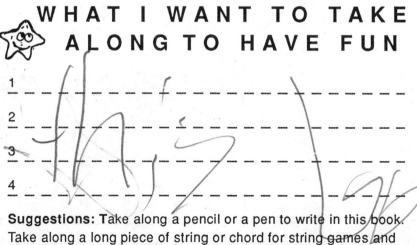

1 _____

2 _____

3 _____

4 _____

Suggestions: Take along a pencil or a pen to write in this book.
Take along a long piece of string or chord for string games and
bring some sheets of paper to make folded things. If you've got a
box of colored pencils, you also can color in this book.

MAKE ZOOMY THINGS
WITH PAPER

FLYING FUN WITH PAPER AIRPLANES

A few simple folds, and you can have a great time with your own paper airplane. Make them. Fly them. Here's how to do it

FRONT   **BACK**

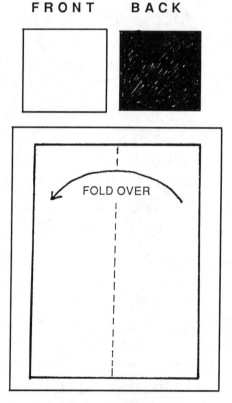

FOLD OVER

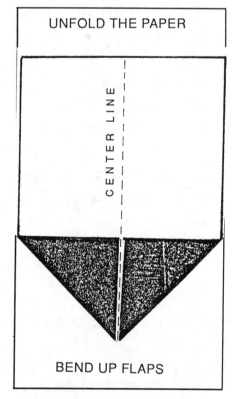

UNFOLD THE PAPER

CENTER LINE

BEND UP FLAPS

1 Take a sheet of typing or other 8 1/2 x 11-inch paper and lay it down. Fold it in half the long way

2 UNFOLD. Turn the paper over. Fold up the bottom corners to touch the centerline.

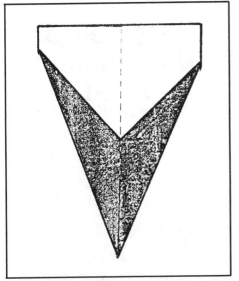

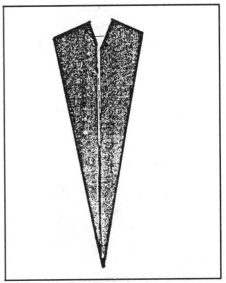

3 Fold it over again. The fold should touch the center line. It's looking like a plane, isn't it?

4 Fold it over again. You have now formed the wings. It's ready!

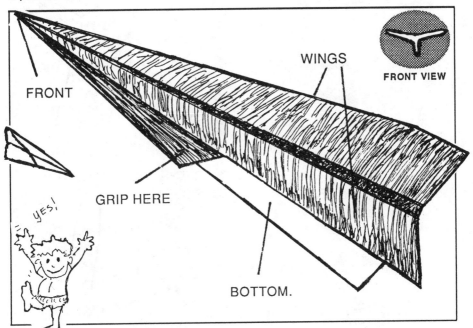

FRONT VIEW

WINGS

FRONT

GRIP HERE

BOTTOM.

yes!

5 Unfold the wings once. They should stand straight out. You now have a paper airplane ready to fly! Grip it with your thumb and forefinger

FUN GAMES WITH YOUR PAPER AIRPLANE— NEXT PAGE

THINGS TO DO WITH YOUR NEW PAPER AIRPLANE

GIVE IT A NAME. COLOR IT.

DRAW A LITTLE PILOT. PASTE OR TAPE IT IN THE CENTER OF PLANE

HOW FAR CAN YOU MAKE IT FLY? HAVE A CONTEST?

FLY IT THROUGH AN OBSTACLE COURSE.

MOST HANG TIME — STAYS ALOFT THE LONGEST

MY FAVORITE THINGS PAGE

Write down the things you **really like to do** while you travel. Then show this page to your adults! (Adults! Take note!)

1 _____

2 _____

3 _____

4 _____

5 _____

6 _____

7 _____

8 _____

TWO-MINUTE AUTHOR

Each player gets a piece of paper and a pencil. When the Editor says GO, each player **writes a story** about his or her **favorite person,** without naming the person. When the Editor calls **STOP,** everybody stops writing, no matter where they are. Then the fun begins. One person starts the game by reading his story, and the others in turn try to guess 1/ What business is the person in and 2/ Who the person is. At the end, the two-minute author gets to tell why he or she selected the person to write about.

BE YOUR OWN NAVIGATOR

You can tell a lot from a map, if you know where to look. Maps are really just scaled down pictures of the real world. They contain a lot of information. With a map, you can find out:

- **what direction you'll go**

- **how far you'll go**

- **where you're going**

- **what you'll see along the way**

- **how long it will take you to get there**

- **other neat stuff**

1/ Which way do you go?
(Direction)

Each map tells **which way** you're going. Look at the map to your right.

- The **top** of the map is **North**

- The **bottom** is **South**

- To your **left** is **West**

- To your **right** is **East.**

Ask your adult for a map they'll use on your trip. Carefully unfold it and hold it in front of you.

Which **way** are you going on your trip?

_____

DIRECTION

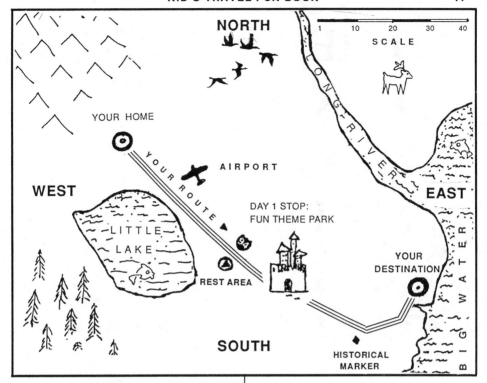

2/ Where are you going?
(Towns, cities)

Have your adult help you find your **home place** on the map. This is where you are starting from.

Then look for the place or places you are going. This is your **destination.**

Have your adult mark your home place and where you are going on the map. Draw a line between the two places. This is your **route.**

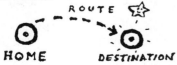

3/ How far are you going?
(Distance)

Get a piece of **string** or a strip of paper.

On your map, lay this between where you're **coming from** (home) and where **you're going** (your destination).

Mark the string or paper.

Lay it on the **distance scale** on your **map** to measure the distance. You can tell how far you have to go to get there. And, you can tell how far you came.

OTHER THINGS THAT MAPS CAN TELL YOU

Here are some of the things you can see on a map

DAY 1 STOP:
FUN THEME PARK

HISTORICAL
MARKER

Fun places such as the Fun Theme Park and the Historical Marker on the map in the last page.

LITTLE LAKE

Lakes and rivers. (These are colored blue on your adult's map). Look for Long River, Big Water and Little Lake on the map.

Interstate Freeways. (Red) A marker showing which interstate you are on. In the map, you are on Interstate Highway 94.

Airport (airplane symbol)

5,000 to 25,000   25,000 to 50,000   50,000 and over

Cities and towns. These are represented by symbols. The shape tells how big some cities are.

```
1     10    20    30    40
          SCALE
```

A **distance scale** shows miles between places. You can measure how far you have to go.

A map will tell you when the next public **Rest Area** will be coming up. It's shown by a triangle inside a circle. You can do more than rest here.

You can tell if there is a **campgrounds state park** Or a **railroad** ahead.

How soon will we get there?

Talk to your adults about the distance you measured on your map. Ask them to estimate how long it will be to get to your destination. Write below:

DAYS

HOURS

A map tells a story

As you travel, you can mark on your own map (the one you drew earlier in this book.) You can draw in some of the interesting towns and things you saw. You can write down the distance you traveled.

Ask your adult. If you travel by car, you can tell how far you went by the speedometer.

You can keep adding to your map to make it tell a story of your travel adventures.

How are you traveling?

How you travel can make a difference in the kind of map you can use. If you are going by car, you can use an ordinary road map that is used by automobile drivers. These show cities, areas, states, or even continents.

If you are going by airplane, train or bus, you may be going a long distance. As you know from maps in your school, some maps show the whole United States or Europe or even the world. These are large-scale maps.

There's a map for nearly every travel purpose, including maps for when you hike in a wilderness or take a trip in a boat. Each map tells you a lot about the places you are going to. It's fun to learn more about maps and to read what they can tell you.

D R A W I N G
A N D
W R I T I N G
I S   F U N
O N   T R I P S

If you jot down a few words, or draw some pictures as you travel, you can capture some special moments in your trip. It's fun to write and to draw about what you saw or did. You'll find some **Write and Draw Pages** throughout your *Kid's Travel Fun Book.*

Just a few words about a travel adventure, happening, or nice thing is worth capturing in your book. *You're* the author. This is *your* book. What made you smile today? What did you do that was fun? Feel special? Made you laugh? Or what did you and your people accomplish that you're proud of?

When your trip is over, you'll have a special place for some of your memories. Be sure to put this book in your personal library so that you can look at it and remember. And be happy with your memories of your trip.

Write and Draw Pages

Write and Draw Pages

DRAW ⭐
SOMETHING
YOU SEE

Draw something you see as you travel. Below your picture, write
a few words about what you drew, such as what your picture is
about and where you first saw it.

WHAT I DREW

WRITE ABOUT YOU

Tell something that happened today that interested you. Did you see a dinosaur? Probably not. But you can have a lot of fun writing about your own travel adventures.

SOME HINTS: When did this happen? Where were you? What were you doing? What did you see? Who did you see? How did you feel? Tell about colors, numbers, movements and actions.

Write and Draw Pages

PUZZLING TOOTHPICKS

Challenge your brain with these games. You'll need some
toothpicks, straws, sticks or pieces of paper that are
long and narrow. Lay them out as shown.

SERIOUS SQUARES

Lay down **12** toothpicks the way we did. You'll have **2**
toothpicks at the top and bottom, **2** on each side,
and **4** in the middle. Got it?

 ## YOUR CHALLENGE

Remove **2,** but only 2, toothpicks
but still leave **2 complete SQUARES.**

DON'T LOOK NOW

...but the answers to the toothpick puzzles are on **page 26.** See if you can figure out
the anwers for yoruself. Work with the toothpicks. You can do it.

NINE SQUARES

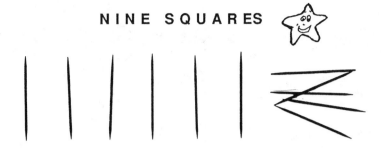

Count out **6** toothpicks and lay them side by side, like we did. You also get **5** more toothpicks to work with. You've got a total of 11 toothpicks.

YOUR CHALLENGE

Your challenge is to USE ALL YOUR TOOTHPICKS to make nine. This is a tricky one.

 # MORE SERIOUS SQUARES

Count out **17** toothpicks and arrange them the way we did. That's with **3 rows** top to bottom, plus **4 rows** side to side. You've got **6 squares**.

YOUR CHALLENGE

Figure out a way to remove only **6 sticks** so that you end up with **2 SQUARES**.

A N S W E R S T O
P U Z Z L I N G
T O O T H P I C K S

(From pages 24 & 25)

SERIOUS SQUARES: Take away **2 toothpicks** as shown. See? You remove the toothpick to the left of center and above the center. The result? You make **2 squares** out of 4.

NINE SQUARES: With **11 t**oothpicks, you've been asked to make **9**. Sound tricky? Take a look below: Add 1 between the 1st and the 2nd toothpicks; do that again between the 4th and the 5th toothpicks, and go crazy laying in 3 more sideways to the right of the 6th toothpick. The result? A REALLY OUTSTANDING **NINE!**

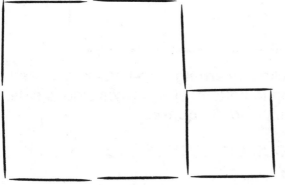

MORE SERIOUS SQUARES: Your task is to take away **6** toothpicks to make **2 squares.** You can do that by removing the outer right and upper right toothpicks as shown as well as the 4 toothpicks in the center of the left hand box. The result is **2 squares.**

F A S T
M O U T H

Here's a game you can play without much thinking! In fact, if you think too much before you play, you probably will lose.

To begin, one person says **a word**. the next person needs to say **another word *without a pause*.** The response should be a word that is connected with the first word. For example, the first player says frog. The next person can say jump. Or green. The next player says another word associated with the word.

Players say words quickly, one after the other, without repeating. The game continues until one player **repeats** a word, says a **wrong** word, or doesn't **immediately** think up a word and gets a funny look on his or her face.

B A D
M O U T H

This game is played like *Fast Mouth,* except that instead of saying a word associated with another, you say just the **opposite.** For example, if someone says **stop,** the next player says **go.** One player says **yes**, the other **no.** What fun! (Especially if you're feeling a little contrary, anyway).

WRITE ABOUT YOU

Just a few words about a travel adventure, happening, or nice thing is worth capturing in your book. *You're* the artist and the author. What made you smile today? What did you do that was fun? Or did that you're proud of? You can have a lot of fun writing about your own travel adventures.

_____

_____

_____

_____

_____

_____

_____

_____

_____

_____

_____

_____

Write and Draw Pages

DRAW SOMETHING YOU SEE

Draw something you see as you travel.

Below your picture, write a few words about what you drew.

WHAT I DREW

_____

_____

Write and Draw Pages

H O W   T O
W R I T E   M O R E
A B O U T   Y O U !

Some helpful hints
and ideas for **you**

On the **Write and Draw** pages, you have a wonderful way to
tell about **you, your trip,** and the **people** with you.

- Write about the **Four W's**: *Who, What, Where* and *When:*

   *My adult and I with baby brother got on the road at 9:30 car
   Wednesday (September 28) from Orlando, Florida. Our destination: Disneyland! (Wow)*

 - Check a **map:**

   *Today we'll drive about 28 miles in our car. Since we'll
   mostly be on the freeway, we'll be there in about half an
   hour.*

- Write about something **interesting** that happened to you.

   *Just inside the park, Mickey M saw us and gave us a big hug.
   I didn't know he was so big! (and furry).*

- Or something **different:**

  The Haunted House was spectacular, complete with ghosts and goblins.

- You can write about what you **ate:**

  At noon, we sat at a picnic table and had hamburgers and root beer.

- Or write about the **weather:**

  Today is full of sunshine and is very warm. It's pretty much like this all year long in Florida. It's hard to think that back home we have snow and ice.

   - You can write about any fun thing you **bought:**

  Had to get a Mouse Cap with big ears. (cost $12.95, from my allowance.) What fun!

- For fun, you can **grade** your trip or vacation. You can write:

  On a scale of one to ten, today was a _____.

- You can tell how you **feel:**

  We all enjoyed today. It was great to be here.

HAVE FUN!

DRAW SOMETHING YOU SEE

Draw something you see as you travel.

Below your picture, write a few words about what you drew.

WHAT I DREW

WRITE ABOUT YOU

Tell something that happened today that interested you.
You can have a lot of fun writing about your own
travel experiences and adventures.

_ _

_ _

_ _

_ _

_ _

_ _

_ _

_ _

_ _

_ _

_ _

_ _

_ _

WRITE AND DRAW PAGES

FIVE GOOD GUESSES!

It's fun to guess things. Write down your guess without looking. If you have a partner, you can see who's the most right.

1/ How fast are we going?

(Don't look at the car speedometer)
My guess_____. Partner's guess _____.
The answer_____ (after looking at speedometer).

2/ How far will we go today?

My guess_____. Partner's guess _____.
The answer_____ (at the end of the day, after checking speedometer).

3/ Time of our next "break" or stop.

My guess_____. Partner's guess _____.
The answer_____ (after looking at clock).

4/ Closest to something.

Pick an object a long distance in front of you. Close your eyes. When you think you are alongside it, you yell NOW! and open your eyes. You get one point for each right NOW.

_____Me   _____Partner

5/ When will we get there today?

My guess_____. Partner's guess _____
The answer_____
(after arriving at destination).

DESIGN YOUR OWN SIGNS

DON'T PET THE
STRIPED PUSSYCAT

You've looked at a gazillion road signs. Isn't it time you designed your own?

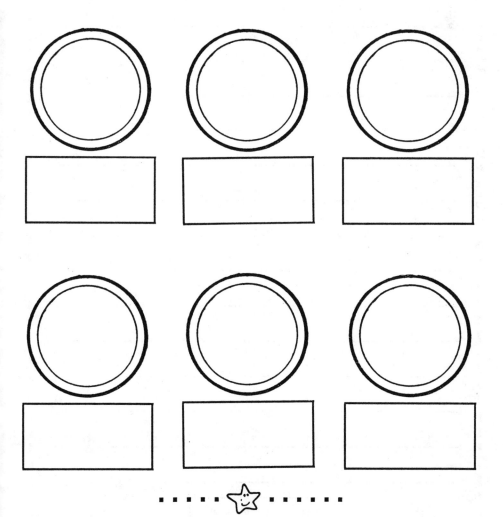

WRITE ABOUT YOU

Tell something that happened today that interested you. You can have a lot of fun writing about your own travel experiences and adventures.

WRITE AND DRAW PAGES

More cats less worry!

HONK
if you
love CATS

CATS
RULE!

CAT
CITY

MEOW
NOW!

DRAW
SOMETHING
YOU SEE

Draw something you see as you travel.

Below your picture, write a few words about what you drew.

WHAT I DREW

_____

_____

MOON
ROCKET

You don't have to be a rocket scientist to see that not all the rockets aimed will hit the moon. Some will miss --- by a millennium.

YOUR CHALLENGE: Find the rocket that's on course and will land on the moon. Hint: take a straight edge of some kind, such as a piece of paper, and align it with the rockets to see how good the scientist's aims are. You can draw a line from the rocket to the moon.

CAN YOU FOLLOW THE LEADER ?

The game is to line up and **exactly** do whatever your group leader does. Here are some ideas: dancing in your seat, batting bugs away, impersonating a cat's, dog's, or a frog's face (be sure to say, *ribit, ribit* like a frog). Or, follow your leader as he or she skips, hops, or jumps, or tries a high-kicking dance. Or (under adult supervision), jump into the swimming pool and make bubbles, dog-paddle across the shallows, walk on your hands underwater, or dive for pennies. You can take turns being the leader.

LICENSED TO GAME

Your assignment, if you choose to undertake it, will be to see how many license plates you can find. Just mark an X.

UNITED STATES

__ALABAMA
__ALASKA
__ARIZONA
__ARKANSAS
__CALIFORNIA
__COLORADO
__CONNECTICUT
__DELAWARE
__DISTRICT OF COLUMBIA
__FLORIDA
__GEORGIA
__HAWAII
__IDAHO
__ILLINOIS
__INDIANA
__IOWA
__KANSAS
__KENTUCKY
__LOUISIANA
__MAINE
__MARYLAND
__MICHIGAN
__MINNESOTA
__MISSISSIPPI
__MONTANA

__NEBRASKA
__NEVADA
__NEW HAMPSHIRE
__NEW JERSEY
__NEW MEXICO
__NEW YORK
__NORTH CAROLINA
__NORTH DAKOTA
__OHIO
__OKLAHOMA
__OREGON
__PENNSYLVANIA
__RHODE ISLAND
__SOUTH CAROLINA
__SOUTH DAKOTA
__TENNESEE
__TEXAS
__UTAH
__VERMONT
__VIRGINIA
__WASHINGTON
__WEST VIRGINIA
__WISCONSIN
__WYOMING

CANADA

__ALBERTA
__BRITISH COLUMBIA
__MANITOBA
__NEW BRUNSWICK
__NEWFOUNDLAND
__NORTHWEST
  TERRITORIES

__NOVA SCOTIA
__ONTARIO
__PRINCE EDWARD ISLAND
__QUEBEC
__SASKATCHEWAN
__YUKON TERRITORY

WRITE ABOUT YOU

Tell something that happened today that interested you.
You can have a lot of fun writing about your own
travel experiences and adventures.

WRITE AND DRAW PAGES

DRAW
SOMETHING
YOU SEE

Draw something you see as you travel.
Below your picture, write a few words about what you drew.

WRITE AND DRAW PAGES

WHAT I DREW

_____

_____

TEN PENNY PUZZLE

Get **10 pennies** and put them into a **triangle** shape as shown. The triangle has a flat base and a point at the top. (If you don't have pennies, you can use pebbles, rocks, pieces of paper, or other small objects.)

YOUR CHALLENGE: Change your triangle so that the base is at the top and the point is at the bottom — an **upside down triangle** — by moving only **3** pennies. Got it? You can only move **3 pennies.**

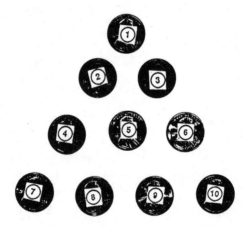

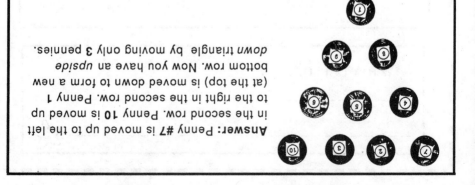

Answer: Penny #**7** is moved up to the left in the second row. Penny **10** is moved up to the right in the second row. Penny **1** (at the top) is moved down to form a new bottom row. Now you have an *upside down triangle* by moving only **3** pennies.

2 x 4
TOOTHPICK
PUZZLE

Take **5** toothpicks and arrange them as shown: **2** toothpicks to the left and **2** toothpicks to the right. In the center lay **1** more toothpick. You now have **2 triangles.**

YOUR CHALLENGE: Take **2** more toothpicks and place them so that you make **4** triangles out of the **2.**

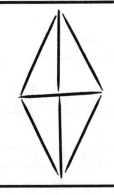

Answer: Add **1** toothpick in the top triangle and **1** toothpick in the bottom triangle as shown. You now have solved the problem and have **4 triangles.**

DRAW SOMETHING YOU SEE

Draw something you see as you travel.

Below your picture, write a few words about what you drew.

WHAT I DREW

_____

_____

WRITE ABOUT YOU

Tell something that happened today that interested you.
You can have a lot of fun writing about your own
travel experiences and adventures.

WRITE AND DRAW PAGES

_ _

_ _

_ _

_ _

_ _

_ _

_ _

_ _

_ _

_ _

_ _

CAT'S CRADLE

Here's a basic string game
passed down through the years.
You'll see why it's fun.

1 Get a long piece of string — about **twice** as long as your arms. Tie a knot in it to make it into a loop.

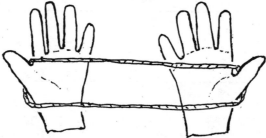

2 Put your loop around your hands as shown. One loop is around your **left thumb**; the other around your **right**. Keep your loop under tension.

3 Move your hand so that you put the string between your **little finger** and **fourth finger** on the **left hand**. Do the same for the **right**. Keep it fairly tight.

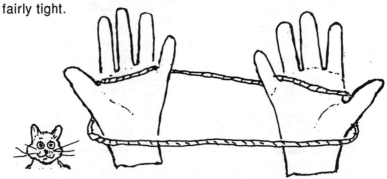

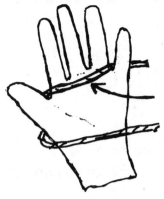

4 Move your **right MIDDLE finger** under the **loop** on your left hand. Pull your hand back tight.

5 Move your left MIDDLE finger under the right hand loop. Pull back.

6 You now have a basic cat's cradle.

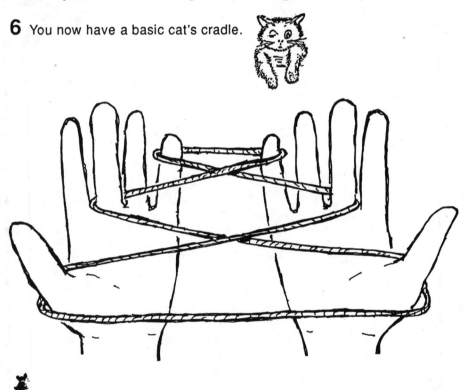

Practice your cat's cradle. Go slow at first, then build up speed. See how fast you can make it. Get another piece of string and challenge a friend to see who can complete their cat's cradle first. You can see why kids all over the world play string games.

DRAW
SOMETHING
YOU SEE

Draw something you see as you travel.

Below your picture, write a few words about what you drew.

WRITE AND DRAW PAGES

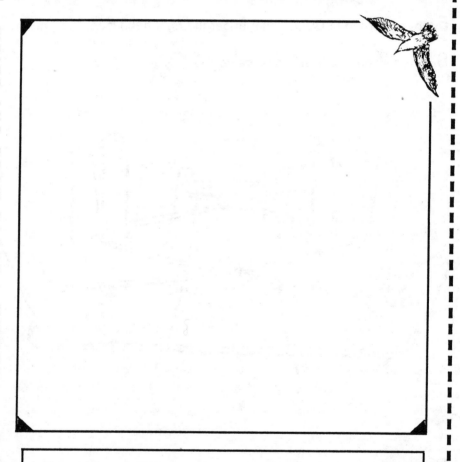

WHAT I DREW

_____

_____

WRITE
ABOUT
YOU

Tell something that happened today that interested you.
You can have a lot of fun writing about your own
travel experiences and adventures.

WRITE AND DRAW PAGES

FLYING BUGS

Hey, now! Bugs are flying around, but they're not all alike. Find the **two** bugs that match.

ANSWERS: 1/ no door handle 2/ no hub caps 3/ has rear bumper 4/ no antenna 5/ SAME AS 9 6/ no headlight 7/ windows are white 8/ flat rear tire 9/ SAME AS 5 10/ one wing 11/ black headlight 12/ no front bumper

FUN WITH CUSTOM LICENSE PLATES

Some people order **special license plates** for their automobiles. These plates show a *name,* a *nickname,* or *tell something* about the driver. Some are **clever** and **funny.** See how many you can find. Write them below.

DRAW SOMETHING YOU SEE

Draw something you see as you travel.

Below your picture, write a few words about what you drew.

WRITE AND DRAW PAGES

WHAT I DREW

_____

_____

WRITE ABOUT YOU

Tell something that happened today that interested you.
You can have a lot of fun writing about your own
travel experiences and adventures.

_____

_____

_____

_____

_____

_____

_____

_____

_____

_____

_____

_____

WRITE AND DRAW PAGES

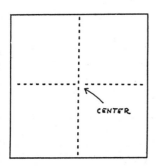

THE AMAZING JUMPING FROG

Here's a fun little frog you can make jump and, if you're handy, even talk (when you supply the voice).

STEPS:

1 Make a square piece of paper. You can simply tear off a part of a piece of typing paper, if you'd like, to make it square.

2 Fold it in half, top to bottom. Run your fingers over the crease. Open it up. Then fold it the other way, from side to side. Again crease it so that the fold is sharp. Open it up again. You now have a square piece of paper with 2 folds, giving you 4 squares. Find the center (where the folds intersect).

3 Fold each of the 4 corners to the center. You now have a smaller square. Run your fingers over the creases so that they are sharp.

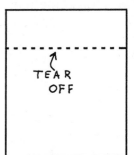

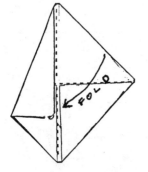

4 Turn your square so that a pointed end is up. Take the left side and fold it so that the edge comes to the center line. Do the right side. Crease them well.

5 Fold the bottom up halfway.

6 Fold the left side in to the center line. Do the same for the right side.

7 Fold up the bottom halfway.

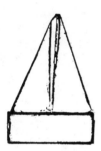

8 Fold the bottom square in half again.

9 Fold the top downward. This forms part of the head.

10 Drawn in eyes and head

PRESS HERE

11 Place your finger on your frog's back, near the bottom. Press down and slide your finger back. Watch your frog jump! Practice your jumps. If you have a partner, see who can make the frog jump farthest. High est. Turn a somersault.

DRAW SOMETHING YOU SEE

Draw something you see as you travel.

Below your picture, write a few words about what you drew.

WHAT I DREW

_ _

_ _

ME?

WRITE ☆ ABOUT YOU

Tell something that happened today that interested you.
You can have a lot of fun writing about your own
travel experiences and adventures.

_ _

_ _

_ _

_ _

_ _

_ _

_ _

_ _

_ _

_ _

_ _

_ _ _ _ _ _ _ _ _ _ _ _ _ _ _ _ _ _ _ _

_ _ _ _ _ _ _ _ _ _ _ _ _ _ _ _ _ _

_ _ _ _ _ _ _ _ _ _ _ _ _ _ _ _ _

Dog-gone!

WRITE AND DRAW PAGES

AMAZING MAZES

Help this family find their way out of this traffic jam. You can go wherever there's an open space. You can't go where a bar or a line blocks your passage. Start at the beginning and keep trying all the mazes.

START

END

AMAZE YOURSELF
WITH YOUR OWN MAZE

On a sheet of paper you can create your own **maze.** A partner can also create a maze to challenge you. Just draw **two sets of lines** representing a place to follow. Be sure to include some dead ends. Mark one place **START** and one place **END.** Test your maze and then give it to the other player. Here's an example:

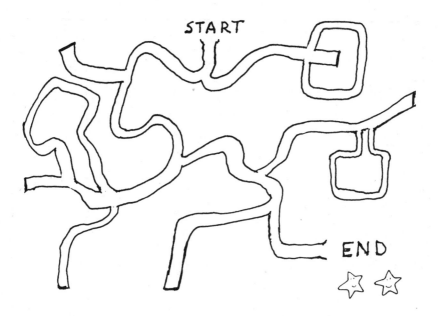

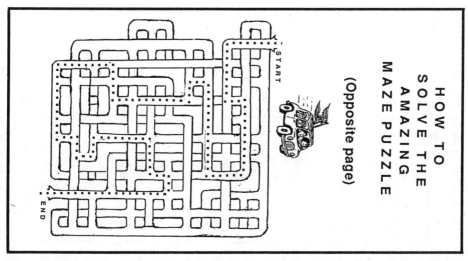

HOW TO
SOLVE THE
AMAZING
MAZE PUZZLE

(Opposite page)

DRAW SOMETHING YOU SEE

Draw something you see as you travel.

Below your picture, write a few words about what you drew.

WRITE AND DRAW PAGES

WHAT I DREW

WRITE ABOUT YOU

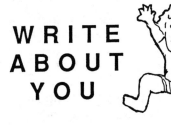

Tell something that happened today that interested you.
You can have a lot of fun writing about your own
travel experiences and adventures.

WRITE AND DRAW PAGES

DUELING WITH DOTS

You can duel with a friend with these **Dueling Dots**. Each person gets **one move** at a time between the dots. You can move up, down, or across linking dots to complete a **square.** You can't move **diagonally.** If you see that your opponent is about to complete a square, you can put your line in and claim the square when it's your turn. The winner is the one who gets the **last line** in to form a **square.**

Round 1/

Round 2/

Round 3/

Round 4/

Round 5/   Round 6/

Round 7/   Round 8/

CLASS ACT

One person selects a **class** or **category** (*colors, movie stars, books, dogs, cats, birds, sports teams, etc.*) and each player takes turns naming something in that class or category. The last player with an answer is the winner. You may want to keep a list of what's been named to keep from repeating names. The winner gets to pick the next class. Be sure to pick a class that everyone will know about.

MAKE THIS FUN

PAPER BALLOON

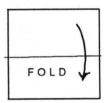

1 Make a paper **square.** Fold it in half. Open it. Then fold it in half the other way.

2 Open the paper up and turn it **over.** Put a **pointed** side up. Fold it from **top** to bottom. Open it up. Then fold it from **side** to side.

3 Unfold it. Using the folds as guides, fold it **inward** (1)so it becomes **star-shaped.** Flatten your star (2). You now have a triangular shaped tent (3).

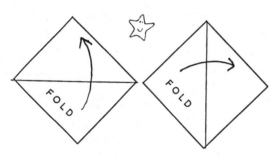

4 You'll have **two flaps** on each side. Fold the **right** side **flap** to the **peak.** Fold the **left** flap to the **top. Turn your triangle over.**

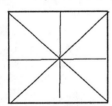

5 Repeat the folds (right and left folds to the **peak.**)

ALL FLAPS UP!

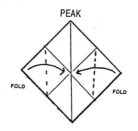

6 You now have a **square** again. Put the peak at the **top** (the closed end). You again have **two flaps** on each side. Fold the **right** flap toward the center. Do the same for the **left** flap.

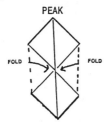

7 Turn the triangle over. Put the peak at the top. Fold the **right flap** to the center. Then fold the **left flap** to the center.

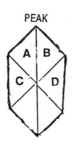

8 You'll see **two loose flaps** at the top, **A & B.** These fold into **pockets C & D**. See the detail. Turn your work over and repeat.

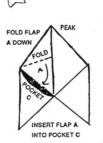

9 You now have **finished** folding. Find the **hole** in the bottom. Blow hard. When your balloon inflates, help it round out with your fingers.

This is a fun balloon — and you made it yourself. It's lightweight, so you can just **toss it** in the air and catch it. Or bat it around. You can **toss** your balloon to a friend and enjoy a game of **catch.** You can play **basketball** with a motel wastebasket or a folded-down paper sack.

A STRING TRICK:

THE
VANISHING
KNOT

Amaze your friends! Astound your adults with this neat string trick. You'll tie a knot in a shoestring. Before their very eyes, the knot will disappear. Alakazam. Zow!

1 Get a shoestring and hold **one end up** in each hand.

2 Tie an **overhand knot** in the center. To tie the knot, just move your **left hand** in a loop around the string as shown..

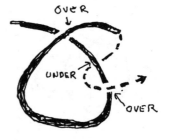

3 You'll end up with a **loose knot** looking like this.

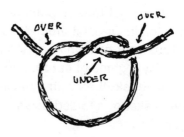

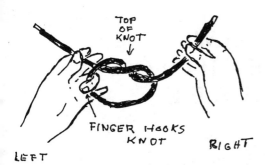

TOP OF KNOT ↓

FINGER HOOKS KNOT

LEFT   RIGHT

4 Hold up the knot. Note that the **backs** of your hands are toward your audience and that your **left hand** is in a closed fist. Secretly slip your **third finger** into the loop.

5 This is what the audience sees as you hold your left hand above your **right hand.** Gently **pull** your right hand **down.** Zow! The knot disappears in front of their eyes.

AUDIENCE VIEW

HAND PULLS DOWN ↓

LEFT

RIGHT

TRICKY!

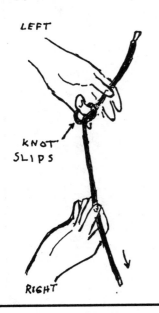

LEFT

KNOT SLIPS

RIGHT

6 What actually happened is that, hidden from the audience's view, the third finger **lets the knot slip** along the shoestring as you pull. The audience sees a whole shoestring, without a knot in it, at the end. You can end the trick by tossing your left hand up, as if throwing away the vanished knot. Then open your left hand to show that it's empty. How'd you do it? You can say, **It's magic.**

HINTS: Practice this trick by yourself until you feel **comfortable** with it. The audience sees the knot you tie at the beginning, but be certain to hold your hands up high enough so that they don't see you slip your finger into the "knot." By appearing to pass your hand over the knot, you make it vanish. Be certain to keep the loop **loose**, so it will slip easily.

DRAW SOMETHING YOU SEE

Draw something you see as you travel.

Below your picture, write a few words about what you drew.

WRITE AND DRAW PAGES ♥

WHAT I DREW

_____

_____

WRITE ABOUT YOU

Tell something that happened today that interested you.
You can have a lot of fun writing about your own
travel experiences and adventures.

❤ --

WRITE AND DRAW PAGES

SAIL THIS PAPER BOAT

You can fold a piece of paper into a classy little boat
that floats and sails (if you supply the wind)

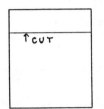

1 Make a square piece of paper.

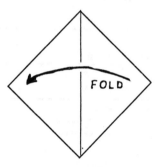

2 Put one pointed end up. Fold
over one side, tip to tip. Crease
the fold really good (and the fol-
lowing folds).

3 Unfold. The crease forms the center
line.

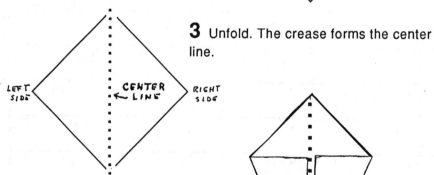

4 Fold the right side to the
center line. Then the left side.

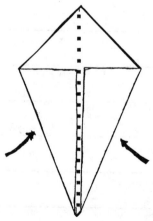

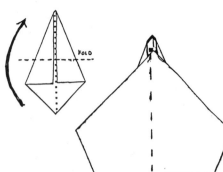

5 Turn it around so that the smallest tip is at the top. Fold the bottom up to touch the top.

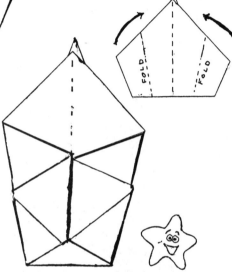

6 Fold the right side to the center line. Then fold in the left side.

7 Take the top layer of folded paper. Fold it down so that its tip touches the bottom, as shown.

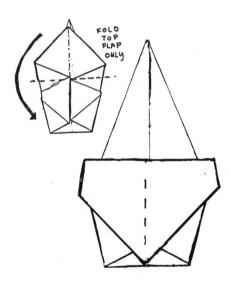

8 Lift the layer you just folded. Bend it upright as shown. This is now your sail.

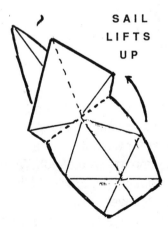

SAIL LIFTS UP

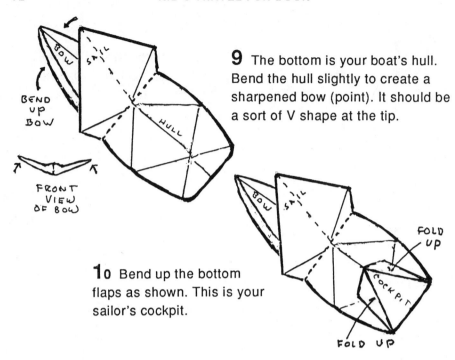

9 The bottom is your boat's hull. Bend the hull slightly to create a sharpened bow (point). It should be a sort of V shape at the tip.

10 Bend up the bottom flaps as shown. This is your sailor's cockpit.

11 Give your little boat a name and decorate it. You can color the sail.

12 Put your boat in some water (a bathtub?) and blow on the sail from behind. Watch it go!

I D E A S : You can make a fleet of these little racers and share them with your companions for sailboat races. These paper boats will last in the water for a number of races before they get waterlogged (depending on the paper you used). We used ordinary computer printer paper, but any quality paper will do, including heavy wrapping paper. When they get too wet to sail, you can let them dry out to sail later. And you easily can make some more. **Fun!**

GAMES TO PLAY

CLASS ACT

One person selects a **class or category** (colors, movie stars, books, dogs, cats, birds, sports teams, etc.) and each player takes turns **naming something** in that class or category. The **last** player with an answer is the winner.

You may want to keep a list of what's been named to keep from repeating names. The **winner** gets to pick the next class. Be sure to pick a class that everyone will know about.

CARPENTER WORDS

The object of this game is to build **as long a word** as you can. The first player chooses a **vowel** (a, e, i, o, u). The second player chooses a **letter** (a consonant) that will spell a two-letter word. The next player chooses **another letter** that will spell a word. Letters can be used more than once and can be rearranged. See how many letters can be added and still be able to form a word from them.

For example: Player One chooses an **A**. Player Two chooses **M**, so the word formed is **AM**. The letters are added on anywhere to form new words: **ARM, FARM, FARMER.**

DRAW SOMETHING YOU SEE

Draw something you see as you travel.

Below your picture, write a few words about what you drew.

WRITE AND DRAW PAGES

WHAT I DREW

_____

_____

WRITE ABOUT YOU

Tell something that happened today that interested you.
You can have a lot of fun writing about your own
travel experiences and adventures.

WRITE AND DRAW PAGES

MAKE A FRIENDSHIP RING

Have a special friend? Here's how you can make a special token of your friendship — a Friendship Ring

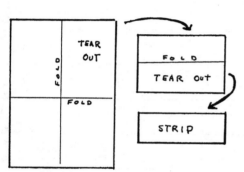

1 Start with a piece of 8 1/2 x 11 paper, then **fold it in half** from **top to bottom.** Then fold it again in **half** side to side. You now have **4** quarters. Tear out **one quarter.** Then **fold that quarter** from side to side, so you have **two long, narrow strips** each measuring about 2 inches by 5 1/2 inches.

2 Fold one strip in **half** the **long way** as shown. **Unfold.** You have a **centerline** down the long strip. Fold **each edge** in to the **centerline.** This creates a **band** about **1 inch** wide.

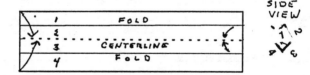

3 Fold the long strip in half again to make a **thin long strip** about 1/2 **inch wide.** You have finished with the band.

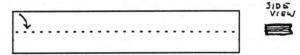

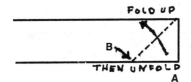

4 **The crown.** On the right side, fold up one corner **Point A** to the top. Then **unfold it.** The bottom fold becomes **Point B**

5 **Fold over** Point **A** to Point **C,** making a square. (If you fold over at the bottom of the previous fold, **Point B,** you'll have a square.)

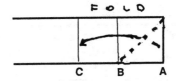

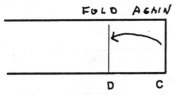

6 **Fold** that square over again, from **Point C** to **Point D.**

7 **Unfold.** Take the **long strip** and give it a **twist** so that it **folds under** to point **E.** You now have an L shape.

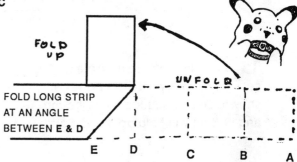

FOLD LONG STRIP AT AN ANGLE BETWEEN E & D

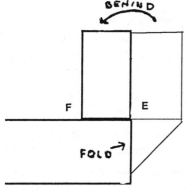

8 **Fold** the L shape again to your left from Point **E** to Point **F.** Note that the fold goes **behind** the band.

9 Fold the upper strip **down** as shown.

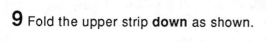

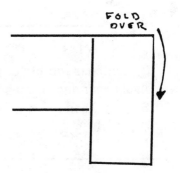

10 **Fold up** once.

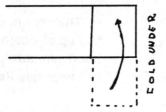

And **fold down** the **end tab**.

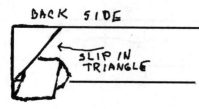

11 **Slip** the square, folded down end into the **triangle** at the back of the long strip. You have created your **crown.** Note that you have a **collar** formed in front.

12 On the left side, fold the **tips** down to make an **arrow** shape.

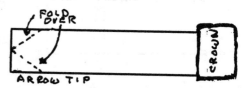

13 Bend the band in a **circle** and insert the arrow tip into the **collar** as shown. Gently squeezing at the top and bottom will help open the **collar.**

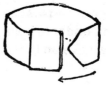

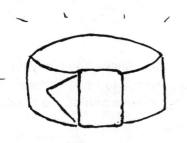

You now have a handsome **Friendship Ring.** Adjust the length to fit. Give it to your friend.

Use a **second strip** to make another, matching ring for yourself.

B I G G E R   O R   S M A L L E R ?

If your ring is **too big** or **too small,** you can easily adjust it. Unfold your ring. Then add or take out another **"square."** (Step 6) Then refold it the same as before. (Steps 7 through 13)

DECORATE YOUR RING

You can decorate your **Friendship Ring** in a number of ways. Use your imagination.

ON THE CROWN

Initials of Friend

Picture of Friend

Two hearts

Stars

A special date

ON THE BAND

Fancy decorations

A date or a place

A pledge or a saying

ON THE INSIDE

Your name and to whom you're giving the ring

A special remembrance or memory

DRAW
SOMETHING
YOU SEE

Draw something you see as you travel.

Below your picture, write a few words about what you drew.

WRITE AND DRAW PAGES

WHAT I DREW

_____

_____

WRITE ABOUT YOU

Tell something that happened today that interested you. You can have a lot of fun writing about your own travel experiences and adventures.

WRITE AND DRAW PAGES

GAMES TO PLAY

LIVE! YOU'RE ON TV

Take turns being a **television news person** on a *live* satellite telecast. To do this, the gamemaster identifies **the news subject** and says, *"You're on,"* and points to a player. That player then gives a **live news type telecast** to viewers. Subjects can include: looking out the window at a cow, a dog sleeping beside the road, a horse in a field, or a car ahead. The announcer needs to **deepen** his or her voice to sound official and talk importantly without hesitation (no *uhs* or *umns* allowed). An *umn* or an *ah* will put a player **out** as will a delay between words of more than a few seconds. A time limit is 20 seconds. Ready? Set? Well...*You're on!*

QUACK UP

Silly phrases are in! Pick a **phrase** and the next player has to **answer only** with the **chosen phrase.** (Make up your own phrases in advance. Here are some examples: Beam me up, Mr. Spock; Lots of luck; Quack, quack; Pikachu. Pika. Chu; or, Look out behind you, Buffy!) For example, someone says: "Want to stop to take a break?" and the player has to respond with the chosen phrase, "Lots of luck." Take turns thinking up phrases and being the gamemaster.

TINY PEOPLE ON YOUR FINGERS

They move. They talk (with a little help)
And they're ALL on your fingers.

1 **Tear out** a piece of paper about **three inches** square.

2 Fold up about a **half inch** of the bottom. This forms a **cuff.**

3 Decorate your little person

4 **Bend** your paper into a **cylinder** shape. Insert one side into the other. The **cuff** will hold it together. Fit it to your finger.

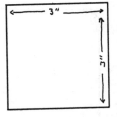

Decorate your puppets into any **figures** you want. You can put on your own **TV show** or **Broadway play,** with you doing the singing and the dialogue.

DRAW SOMETHING YOU SEE

Draw something you see as you travel.

Below your picture, write a few words about what you drew.

WRITE AND DRAW PAGES

WHAT I DREW

_____

_____

WRITE ABOUT YOU

Tell something that happened today that interested you.
You can have a lot of fun writing about your own
travel experiences and adventures.

WRITE AND DRAW PAGES

GAMES TO PLAY

HURRY UP SUNDOWN

When will the **sun go down?** On vacation, the days are long and beautiful, but sunset can be a *special* time. To play this game, everyone **picks a time** on when the sun is **fully down** — out of view. Someone with a watch determines the winner.

Note: The game is over when the sun is fully out of view. Be certain not to look directly into the setting sun to prevent any possible eye damage.

Other variations: You can take turns naming the many **colors** of the sky as the sun goes down. *Red, gold, blue, purple?* You might see these beautiful colors and many more.

SING SONG

Ho! Ho! Everyone **sings** in this game. To start, someone picks a well known tune, jingle or nursery rhyme, such as *London Bridges Falling Down*, and sings it through once.

After that, everyone has to **stop talking,** but only **sing** what they have to say to the tune of the song. Want a snack? Sing it. Want to go to the bathroom. Well, you get the idea. Set a time limit.

WHAT FUN, CHARADES!

Am I out of my mind? No, I'm only playing **charades!** Charades lets players act out all sorts of fun things **without** saying any words. The other players get to guess what the player is trying to tell them.

To **start** charades, the player chooses a **category.** This can be movie, TV or rock stars, favorite cartoon characters, titles of movie or TV programs, book titles, popular sayings, or song titles.

The player holds up the number of fingers for the **words** of the **category.** A **four**-word movie, for example, would take **four** fingers. The player holds up one finger, indicating the **first** word, and then proceeds to act out the word.

If the name or title is **one word**, it can be broken down into **syllables.** For example, let's say you have chosen a **one-word** name to do a charade on. You'd say name and hold up **one** finger. To indicate the syllables, you'd hold up fingers to show the number. For example, you decided to act out the name, *Pokemon.* You'd hold up three fingers for three syllables. Then you'd act it out, first holding up **one** finger, *first* syllable, and act as if you're giving somebody a *poke.* When the players get it, you nod and hold up **two** fingers for the *second* syllable. Here you might point dramatically to yourself. The players would guess, "Me?" For the *last* syllable, hold up your **third** finger and point to a man. Or a boy, but indicate pantomime bigger and older. Circle your hand slowly, indicating all together, and hold up first finger **(poke,)** then second finger **(me)** and then third finger **(man).** They should get it by now. *Fun, huh?*

DRAW SOMETHING YOU SEE

Draw something you see as you travel.

Below your picture, write a few words about what you drew.

WRITE AND DRAW PAGES

WHAT I DREW

_____

_____

WRITE ABOUT YOU

Tell something that happened today that interested you.
You can have a lot of fun writing about your own
travel experiences and adventures.

WRITE AND DRAW PAGES

HELP DESIGN A 4 X 4

Twinkle, the star, needs your help designing a really neat 4 x 4 sports utility wagon. Here are some of the things he'd like to have. Add to them. You can draw your designs below. Maybe you want a sport-ute for around town — another for bashing around the boonies

Twinkle's list of options:

- Big wheels
- Door handle
- Headlights
- Radio antenna
- Roof rack
- Two-tone paint

- Rear View mirror
- Crash Bars
- Roof-top spotlights
- Bumper foglights
- Extra Gas can
- Pennant pole

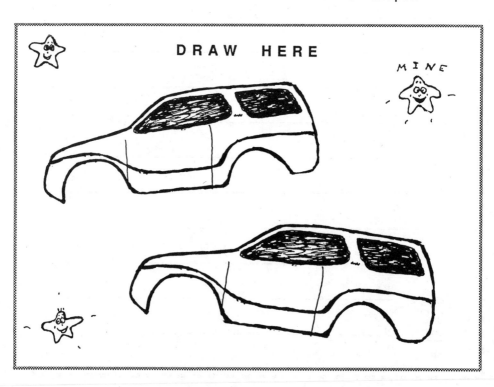

DRAW HERE

MINE

RIGHT HAND
Shows scale of 1 to 4.

LEFT HAND
Tells whether its good or bad

FUN
WITH
FINGERS

Here's a fun **sign language** you and your fellow travelers can enjoy. You can tell each other how well you like or dislike things — without words.

RIGHT HAND
with left hand **THUMB UP**

LEFT HAND
(controls **winner** or **loser** status)

- 4 fingers: can't get much better. *Best rating you can give.*
- 3 fingers: way cool
- 2 fingers: Okay, but so-so
- 1 finger: A yawner. A good one to stay away from. Least favorable of the good ratings.

Thumb **UP:**
good

Thumb **DOWN:**
not good
A BUMMER

RIGHT HAND
with left hand **THUMB DOWN:**

- 4 fingers: barfo. bummer to the max. *Worst rating.*
- 3 fingers: grosses me out
- 2 fingers: pretty bad. May have some good qualities, but these elude me right now.
- 1 finger: really not good. Bummer. *Least objectionable worst rating.*

That's a big thumbs up.
Way up!

OH, NO!
NOT
THAT
GAME!

Here's a game that will drive you *wild!* That's because, no matter what **anyone asks** or **says** in a conversation for the next hour, **no one** can say **yes** or **no**.

You can **answer**, of course. But you **can't say yes or no.** *Got the idea?* The fun comes when people forget **not** to use the no-no words **(yes** or **no)**, or get tricked into using them.

Hints: You can **vary** the game by putting your own **time limit** on how long to play. Or what **penalties** those who forget the game will have if fhey miss.

WHERE
IN THE WORLD
IZ IT?

The first player takes a map and **picks a town** in the direction you're going. The player gives a **clue,** such as "this is a city between Sunnydale and Mayberry on the road we're on" and then challenges, *"Where izit?"* Each city should be within about 150 miles of where you are.

The object: to **find** the city or place. An **alternative:** Use a **different** map to challenge your players to find a different **city, place** or **thing.** If you're in a city, for example, you can ask them to find a particular street. Or if you're out on a highway, you can ask them to find the next rest stop. Airport. *Whatever.*

FUNNY YOU SHOULD ASK THAT

You set up a certain **answer** that players have to answer
questions with. *No matter what!*
The results can be *amazing.*

For example, if you pick the phrase, *"who cut the cheese?"*
to be the answer to everything for Player A, then that player
has to answer **any question** with that phrase. For example,
if player A is asked, "Do you want to stop for ice cream?", the
player **can't answer yes or no,** but only: *who cut the
cheese?"*

Get the idea? You can assign different *phrases* to different
players for loads of fun. Make up your own phrases in
advance.

DIFFERENT NAMES

Some people take pride in **naming things** a little **differently.**
Some are intended to be humorous and some are kind of
poetic. See how many **you can find** and write them below:

_____

_____

_____ MINE

_____

SPECIAL MEMORIES OF MY TRIP

Draw something you saw that you want to remember from this trip

WRITE AND DRAW PAGES

WHAT I DREW

_____

_____

A FEW
SPECIAL
WORDS

Did you have a good time? What was especially memorable? Or not so memorable? Sum up a special few words below to help you remember this trip.

WRITE AND DRAW PAGES

On a scale of 1 (worst) to 10 (best), I'd rate this trip a _____